ACTION MAN

DANGER UNLEASHED

NO MAN'S LAND!

NO MAN'S LAND!
Mission Log: A part of the city has been taken over. The people are imprisoned by electric fence, and a thick fog covers the area. Can Action Man help?
Don't worry, I'll find a way inside.
We're counting on you, Action Man.
Does that thing bite?
GRRRR!
Good luck!
Thanks. Let's catch some bad guys!

I bet those aren't the only rats I'll be meeting today.
The exit should be straight ahead.
Phew! The sewer smelt better than this fog!
You shouldn't be out at this hour, creep!
B-but I'm only a kid...
CLUNK
Gah!
Ungghnn!
Aggh!
Huh?
They needed a rest!
Wow!

Where are your mum and dad?
The emperor's men took them away.
The emperor?
C'mon!
Mum! Dad!
Help!
Shut up, kid! They're coming with us!
Yeah, he's making everyone join his gang.
Can I meet this emperor?
Why? Do you want to join his gang?
No, but my dog's hungry for a taste of the **emperor's ankles!**
Wicked, Action Man!
Suddenly, this doesn't look so easy...

Slaves! Bow down before your emperor, Dr X!
Dr X! Of course!
You know him?
We're free man, not slaves! Run for it!
Stop him!
That's my dad! Save him!
Don't worry!
Sit up and beg...
...good dog!
Destroy them all!

For freedom!
It's coming, it's coming!
More smog! If they can't see, they can't fight!
Ughnn!

Sniff them out, Cyber-dog!
Make way for Action Man and his dog!
CRUNCH!!

This time we've won, Gangrene. Nothing can stop us!
Great, boss!
Aggh!
Aagh!
Don't you like dogs, X?
Get him off me!
Now to switch off the electric fence!
That's no ordinary power, Action Man!

The fence is powered by lightning!
Tempest!
What are you doing?
OK, you're dreaming!
KLUNK
Nooo! Tell me I'm dreaming!
Thanks, kid, you were very helpful.
The rest of 'emperor' X's gang are soon rounded up.
POLICE
Anytime, Action Man. Dad, can we get a dog?
We'll have to think about that, son!
End

SHARK ATTACK!

South Pacific. Naval research ship **Ranger** sinks in a storm. Its valuable cargo – a vital computer chip – is lost in the ocean.
SHARK ATTACK!
ZZZAKK!
How can I hope to find this chip in such shark-infested waters?!

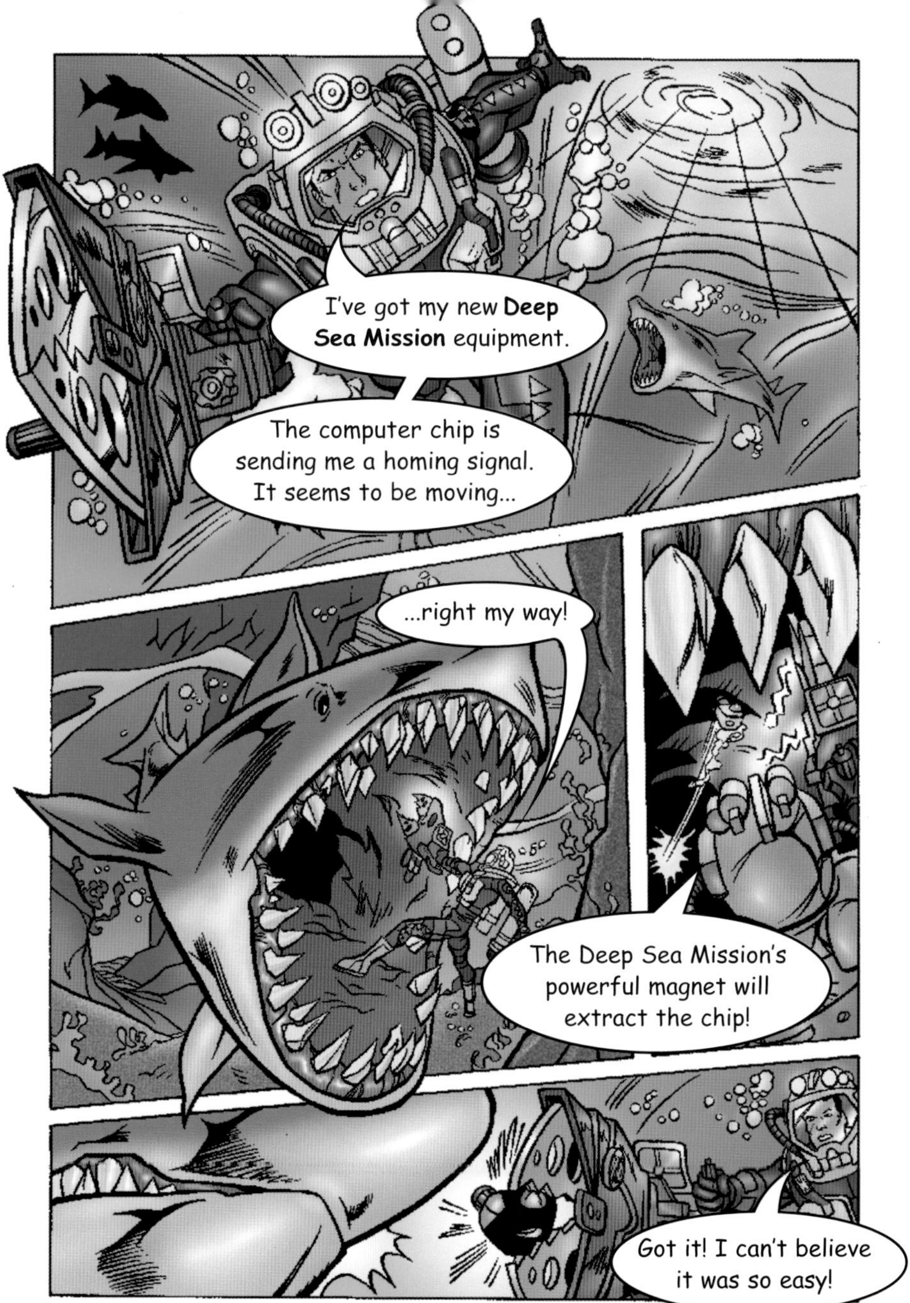
I've got my new **Deep Sea Mission** equipment.
The computer chip is sending me a homing signal. It seems to be moving...
...right my way!
The Deep Sea Mission's powerful magnet will extract the chip!
Got it! I can't believe it was so easy!

But on board Action Man's ship, Tempest has taken control!
I sank the Ranger and I will have the chip and its secrets!
Now to give Action Man a stormy welcome!
Tempest creates a violent whirlpool...
What?

Action Man is sucked out of the sea!
The device mustn't fall into enemy hands!
Oooff!
THDUNK!
SHAAKK!
A shock for you, Action Man!
Tempest's lightning bolt knocks Action Man unconscious.
Now I have the chip!
Action Man is all washed up!

The cold ocean wakes Action Man up.
Quick – cut the anchor chain...
Got to think fast, or I'll be fish food!
...then wrap it round the propeller.
Now to get Tempest's attention...
Hi, Sparky!

I'll teach you, Action Man!
SHZAKK!
Action Man is unhurt, but the blast is just enough to send the sharks packing!
Hey Tempest, when you took my boat, did you read the safety guide?
What?
SNIK!

First, secure the sail!
Nooo!
Aaargh!
Tempest hits the water – with explosive results.
SHRAAAKK!
Back on board...
The propeller's clear, Action Man, but what about Tempest?
Oh, leave him...
Zzzzzz!
...he's **sparked out!**
End

SWARM!

SWARM!

Mission Log: **Tokyo, Japan**. A busy city never sleeps, and neither can Action Man. He's checking out a satellite report on Gangrene.
Arrrgh!
City life can really get you down!

Underground...
Goodbye, Action Man. My warriors will see to you!
Nothing can stop my brilliant plan!
The Japanese love tiny things. They'll die for this miniature cyber-swarm!

Meanwhile...
These guys are tough...
...but not tough enough for the **Tokyo Extreme**!
THWIPP!
What? Hnngh!
Now for the other two...
SHLEK!

Uh-oh...
Uggnn!
Safe at last...
I spoke too soon!
Luckily the Extreme can be used as an outboard motor.
I'm fast – not **fast food!**
CHSSSH!

Time for answers!
Gangrene! So the satellite report was right!
You can't stop me, Action Man!
SLEK!
My cyber-bugs are loaded with sleeping gas.

BZZZZZZZ!
The swarm will send the whole city to sleep.
Tokyo will be mine!
THWIPP!
I don't think so, Gangrene...
...get a buzz out of this!
SMESSH!
Noo! The swarm will attack anything once it's free!

He's right – they'll come after me too.
SHLEK!
But the Tokyo Extreme can handle anything!
BZZZT! SPKOW!
Soon, the evil swarm is finished...
Where's Gangrene got to?
They say the city never sleeps, but Gangrene will be out for a while!
End